Joe's Bar

JOE'S BAR (1)
ISBN: 1 85286 035 9

Published by
Titan Books Ltd,
58 St Giles High St,
London WC2H 8LH.

First Titan Edition January 1988
10 9 8 7 6 5 4 3 2 1

British edition by arrangement with Catalan
Communications, 43 East 19th Street, New York,
N.Y. 10003, USA.

Translation by Jeff Lisle.
Edited by Bernd Metz.
Design by Catalan Communications.

Printed and bound in Spain by JTV-Alvagraf
Dep. L. B. 32.065/87

MUÑOZ **SAMPAYO**

Joe's Bar

TITAN BOOKS

LONDON

Muñoz & Sampayo: A Profile

WHENEVER I read-look at a comic strip story that really interests me (which doesn't happen very often), I realize that what is in front of me cannot be translated into any other visual expression but a comic strip. The story is using, exploring and pushing the language of comic strips, creating an exciting visual event and an exchange of experiences that I am part of. If this sounds rather defensive, it's because it is; what I am defending is the potential of an incredible language as an art form.

But the reality, I feel, is that what ninety percent of comics communicate is irrelevant. Why irrelevant? Because I cannot detect any critical involvement of the creators in what they are producing. I can detect the hands that make the story and the drawing, but not the idea behind them sustaining that frame, nor the personal emotions or commitments toward that frame, toward the story, toward the language.

Comics have certainly developed some extraordinary visual sophistication and ever more pleasant pretty artwork. As the pictures get more stylistically pretty, we are gradually being pushed into a corner where visual amnesia rules. The lives of these picture stories are ephemeral because they don't provide a challenge, they don't carry the possibility of an exchange between creator and reader of a certain feeling, an idea, a sensibility. Just mindless pretty pictures. I don't respect any comic strip, no matter how attractive, if I can't feel any commitment from the creators toward each frame. Without a position, all is lost.

Comic strips are a visual graphic language which allows us to explore our emotions, to deal with our ideas and communicate them. When a new story by Carlos Sampayo and José Muñoz comes my way, whether I like it or not is just a question of taste and that's not important. What is important is that in every story they always have a very strong clear point to put across and a clear idea of how they want to express it, They demand more of their audience than most. They demand an exchange from you, your concentration. Your expectations of how to read-look at a comic strip have to be updated. Their stories repay a second reading. Each frame has a world of its own, operating on different levels. One level is the actual story, but behind all the levels they are creating another story—a mood. You are involved in the world of Muñoz and Sampayo.

Theirs is an oppressive black and white world. Muñoz's drawings, his characters, settings, small details that people his frames, are not there to fill the frame with apologies. They are a vital part of the story. Sometimes they are the story. Every visual element, even the smallest one, is a protagonist that fights to be listened to, gradually becoming a threatening presence that haunts you, full of screams, the most articulate way to express the overwhelming sense of anxiety that permeates their frames, their stories, our way of living. Muñoz's black and white unleashes unique images, because they come directly from his experiences and his dialogues between his heart and the black ink. Above all they are expressed with passion.

All their characters living in New York are peripheral to society; they are unable to understand society, so they react against it. Muñoz and Sampayo had been creating stories about the Big Apple for ten years before they actually visited the city. Their vision of New York may or may not be accurate. Nevertheless I do believe in the world they have created there. It's a world within another world, populated by human beings from different countries who felt alienated in their own homelands, or were pushed out of their countries, but still feel like foreigners in New York. They bring with them different personal geographical maps in their lives. In a sense Muñoz and Sampayo's interpretation of New York is the story that underlies much of their work—people in transit encountering each other with different languages, stories, sunsets.

The way Sampayo edits his text and balloons seems to mirror the fragmentary nature of many of these encounters—conversations begun halfway, left unfinished. You become aware that what Carlos Sampayo decides not to say is as important as what he says. He leaves room for you to do more than consume a story. The silences in his frames are part of the story; they demand reflective concentration, they demand that you stay with it.

A comic strip is a marriage of words and pictures in a series of frames. Yet there is usually one over-rated partner—the pictures, at the expense of the story-line. This dominance of the visual aspect ensures that the comic strip remains stuck in a narrow, limited, provincial vacuum.

Muñoz and Sampayo are trying to create a true marriage between words and pictures, pictures and words, pushing the language of comics to deal with their emotions, their ideas. There are moments in their work that affect me deeply. What I am witnessing is a formidable comic strip. Today, for me, that is a privilege.

Oscar Zarate

MARCH 1971, EZEIZA AIRPORT, Buenos Aires, Argentina. Artist José Muñoz and writer Carlos Sampayo meet for the first time thanks to the departure of their mutual friend, Oscar Zarate. They promise to get together the following week. It will be three years before they see each other again.

In 1972, owing to the political situation in Argentina, both of them move to Europe. In the summer Sampayo leaves for Spain, where he writes scripts, but not his own; he's writing copy for advertising agencies. Muñoz has been drawing comics but not his own; he works as a studio assistant to Solano Lopez. In December he breaks with Lopez and moves to London where he washes plates, reads Chandler, cycles in Regent's Park and draws adventure strips for I.P.C.

1973 and both of them approach 30. Hugo Pratt, one of Muñoz's former teachers in Buenos Aires, advises him to «Do something of your own». Sampayo meantime quits the advertising world, travels in Africa and returns to Spain to hack out eight books in a year for a commercial publishing house.

May 1974, London. Muñoz is bound for Spain and Zarate suggests he look Sampayo up and try doing something with him. From their second meeting in Castelldefels near Barcelona, they begin a remarkable creative friendship that has endured and matured over thirteen years.

Their first character is Alack Sinner, a former New York cop who quits the police force, disgusted by their corruption, to become a private eye. In one episode Alack Sinner meets Sophie, a Polish anarchist, who in her own stories gets caught up in a revolution in Mexico. The lives of the people who frequent Sinner's favorite watering hole, Joe's Bar, fill another series of short stories. Two of these have been translated in *Raw 3* and *6*. Four others are published in this volume.

Paul Gravett

PEPE, THE ARCHITECT

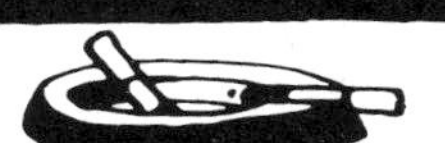

THAT BROAD... JOHNSON ...THEY SAY THAT THE BOSS HAS THE HOTS...
NOW WHO'S THAT GUY GONNA GET IT ON WITH?... HE'S GOT SYPH...
LISTEN, PAL. GOOD OLD JONATHAN JONES CAN GET ANYTHING, ABSOLUTELY ANYTHING YOU NEED!
...ME.
AND WHO'S HE?
LOOK AT RAFF. THEY SAY THE WOMAN'S GETTING IT ON WITH THE BOSS.
OH, YEAH?... TELL ME MORE!
I'm Proud
6 P.M.

...MY STOMACH HURTS!
AND WILL YOU TAKE ME TO YOUR PLACE NOW, ESBIRRO?
I LIVE IN A HOTEL, BABY. BETTER IF WE GO OVER TO YOUR PAD...
8 P.M.

THOSE SURREALISTIC MONSTERS GRÜNEWALD CREATES ARE PRETTY CONTEMPORARY, BUT ENSOR'S ARE FROM WAY BACK...
YES, BUT MALRAUX AND EVEN HAUSER...
Telaraaaaña no tieneii tela...raññaa...
LET'S GO EAT AT THE CHILEAN RESTAURANT. THE INTI ILLIMANI ARE PLAYING TONIGHT AND IT'S ONLY $30 EACH.
LISTEN, PAL, I WAS IN THE FIRST, SECOND AND EVEN THE KOREAN WAR... AND AS A SERGEANT, TOO! ANYONE WHO WANTS TO MAKE SOMETHING OF HIMSELF HERE CAN DO IT ONLY BECAUSE WE FOUGHT THOSE WARS TO KEEP TO WORLD FREE, AND THAT'S THE TRUTH...
MUMMY
10 P.M.

..traigo notas de cariño para todos mis hermanosss..!
11,30 P.M.

VAN GOGH, THAT'S THE GUY WHO...
YOU'RE A PIECE OF SHIT. A PIECE OF SHI-IT!
...FROM MARION THAT...WHEN HE GOT BACK FROM VIETNAM...
Unoo, doss, treees, tus pasos en la escalera, oigo la voz de madera..
de la escale-raaaaaaa..
YEAH, OKAY... IF THAT'S HOW YOU FEEL ABOUT ME I THINK I'LL JUST WALK OUTTA HERE... AND CALL THE COPS!
1 A.M.

Pepe
2,45 A.M.

MARY... AND NOW WHAT DO I DO WITHOUT...?
... OF ALL DAYS...
WILL IT BE A SIN?...I JUST WONDER...WILL IT BE A SIN?
FOLKS... WE'RE CLOSED!
... OOD NIGHT.
HERE I AM IN THE BAR, AND THE CATS DON'T HAVE ANYTHING TO EAT...

TRY TO MOVE YOUR ASS, KID, THESE PIGS HAVE TRASHED THE PLACE WORSE THAN EVER...
UHHUH...

UHHUH, UHHUH... YOU'RE ALWAYS SAYING UHHUH... FOR ONCE I'D LIKE TO HEAR YOU SAY SOMETHING THAT MEANT ANYTHING... SOR...

... SORRY... WELL... EXCUSE ME. WHAT THE HELL DO MY EMPLOYEES' LIVES MATTER TO ME?
THE TRUTH IS THAT I DON'T HAVE MUCH TO SAY... THAT'S ALL.

SEE YA TOMORROW.
PEPE, LISTEN TO ME...

SHOOT...

... YOU'VE BEEN WORKING FOR ME FOR THREE MONTHS AND I'M REAL PLEASED... WHY NOT?... IT'S JUST THAT YOU WORRY ME A LITTLE. JUST A LITTLE, DON'T MAKE A BIG DEAL OUT OF WHAT I'M SAYING...
AND SO?

...IF YOU'VE GOT MONEY PROBLEMS, I'LL GIVE YOU A RAISE. YOU SURE DESERVE IT... BUT IF IT'S ABOUT A WOMAN, TELL ME AND I'LL...
... I'LL TAKE THAT RAISE AND THANKS...

HI, JOE! HOW'S BUSINESS?
AND HOW DO YOU THINK IT'S GOING? A LITTLE TOO WELL, IF YOU ASK ME.
... WOMEN, IN FACT...

AND THIS LITTLE GUY HERE?... IS HE A REGULAR EMPLOYEE OR...?

PEPE, THE CLEAN-UP GUY AT JOE'S, IS SCARED BY THE SUDDEN ENTRANCE OF THE POLICE.

(NOW THEY'RE ASKING ME FOR DOCUMENTS I DON'T HAVE. THEY HAUL ME OFF TO THE PRECINCT, BEAT ME UP, GIVE ME THE THIRD DEGREE, THEN DUMP ME IN THE BACK OF A CELL WHERE I SPEND THE REST OF MY LIFE...)

WHAT DID YOU DO IN YOUR COUNTRY?
... ARCHITECT.

THEY BUSTED PEPITO THE ARCHITECT'S ASS.

... IT'S JUST THAT I DIDN'T WANT TO LEAVE WITHOUT FINISHING IT ALL ...
THEN YOU CAN'T EVER GO!
THAT'S WHAT YOU THINK.

NEW YORK TIMES!... JOHNSTON... MURDERER EXECUTED!... NEW YORK TIMES!!
U.S. MAI

PEPE'S FREE TIME BEGINS WHEN HE GOES TO SLEEP. (IT'S A STACCATO SLEEP. I WAKE UP TO PISS MORE THAN 10 TIMES AND I KEEP THINKING I HEAR THEM COMING UP THE STAIRS AND POUNDING ON THE DOOR...)

MORE, MORE, MORE!!!

(AFTER 5 HOURS, LUCKILY I WOKE UP...)

...GOOD MORNING.

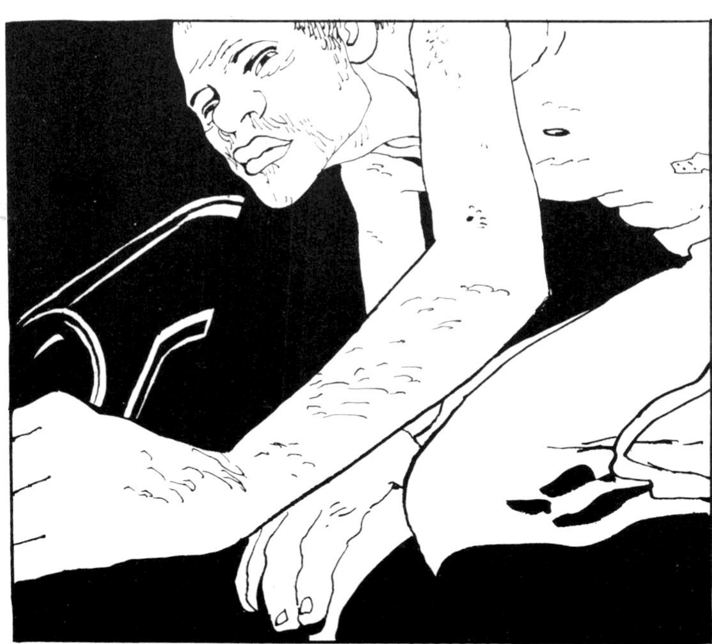

CAN I COME IN ?
COME IN ?... OH, YEAH, SURE... SORRY !

I REALLY LIKE YOU A LOT AND I DON'T KNOW WHY. YOU NEVER LEAVE, WE'VE NEVER GONE FOR A WALK TOGETHER, OR TO A PARK, NOT EVEN A MOVIE...
... IT'S JUST THAT I...
(AND IF YOU WERE FROM THE WOMEN'S POLICE CORPS, IMMIGRATION UNIT ?)

Ohoo nooo..!

I DON'T KNOW WHY YOU KEEP INSISTING... YOU CAN SEE THAT I CAN'T GET IT UP !
... SO WHAT ?... NOW YOU'LL CALM DOWN...

AT 2 A.M., PEPE WATCHES THE LATE NEWS BEFORE GOING TO WORK.
...BECAUSE OF TODAY'S ASSASSINATION OF AMBASSADOR ALZAGA ANCHORENA, THE FBI IS SEARCHING THE AREAS OF THE CITY WHERE EMIGRANTS FROM THAT COUNTRY LIVE. MANY OF THEM ARE SAID TO BE OPPONENTS OF HIS REGIME...

... NOW THEY'RE GOING TO CAPTURE ME, ACCUSE ME, DEPORT ME, TORTURE ME AND CONDEMN ME TO DEATH.
CLICK!

BLOOD BANK
DONORS PAID
AT 2:15 A.M. PEPE LEAVES HIS ROOM TO GO TO WORK.
SUCK ME

DONT WALK
YL001

WHAT'S THAT GUY OVER THERE DOING ?

HELL... HE MUST BE SMASHED.

I CAN'T LET ANY OF THIS STUFF GET TO ME...
Screwed UP

...I'VE GET TO KEEP THE LITTLE SANITY I'VE GOT LEFT...
10

VISA ?
GREEN CARD ?

3 A.M.

HI.

EVENIN'...

WE'RE CLOSING, FOLKS!

(I LOOK AT HIM)

(SHE LOOKS AT ME)

(WHAT'S SHE LOOKING AT?) DOES SHE LOOK AT HIM?

4:20 A.M.
SEE YA TOMORROW, JOE.

SHE WAITS FOR HIM.

GUM

17101

NO, NO, NOOO !!

WHERE DO YOU LIVE?

(WHERE?)
I... I DON'T KNOW... OKAY, THE STREET, SURE... BUT I DON'T REMEMBER THE NUMBER...

... BU... BUT, WHY... WHY DO YOU WANT TO KNOW?

BECAUSE I PLAN ON COMING WITH YOU!

TWO MORE BLOCKS AND THEN TURN LEFT.
OKAY. NOW WHAT...?

WELL, THANKS...
NO, NONE OF THIS THANKS STUFF. I'M GOING WITH YOU!

GIMME THE KEY. I'LL OPEN IT!

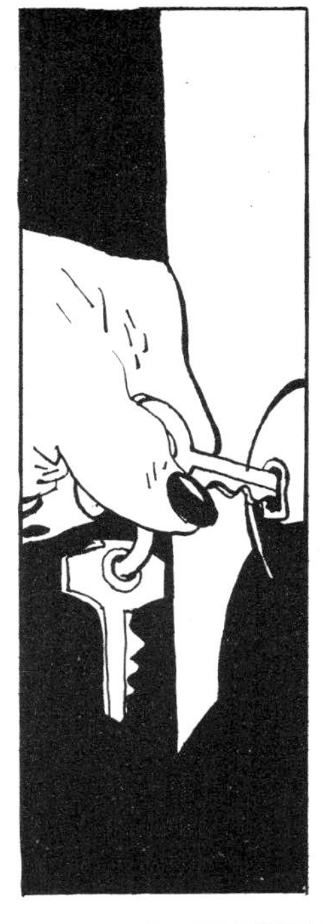

EVEN THOUGH I'VE NEVER SEEN YOU BEFORE, I KNOW EVERYTHING ABOUT YOU. YOU ARE AN ILLEGAL ALIEN WITHOUT A GREEN CARD AND YOU'VE GOT AN UNDER-THE-TABLE JOB. YOU DON'T HAVE ANY FRIENDS OR MONEY... AND, MAYBE YOU'VE EVEN GOT SOME SORT OF PERSECUTION COMPLEX.

HOP IN THE SACK! AND MAKE IT SNAPPY!

I WAS LOOKING FOR YOU ALL NIGHT. I HAD TO CRUISE 20 BARS IN ORDER TO FIND YOU.

ME?
Mamá, papá y...yo..!
17.1.57

SOMEONE LIKE YOU. SOMEONE WHO ONCE HAD IT TOGETHER AND IS TRYING TO GET BACK ON HIS FEET.

BUT YOU'RE MORE INTERESTING TO ME WITH-OUT A PAST... IN LIMBO.

NONEXISTENT...

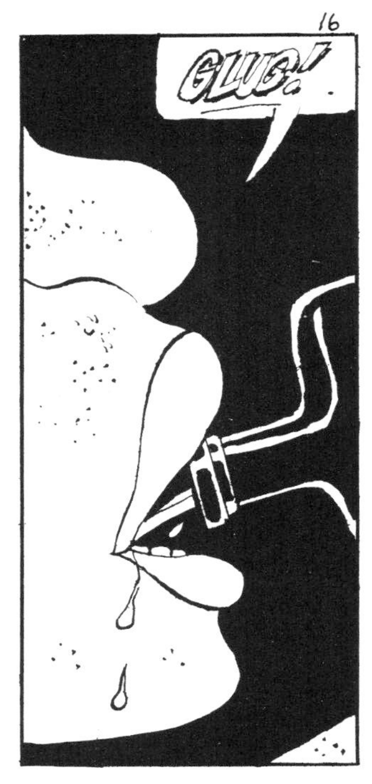
GLUB!

...FINISHED...

I'VE GOT THE MUNCHIES!

CRUN
CR

HEY... YOU DON'T LIKE ME?

YOU'RE NOT THE ONLY PERSON IN THE WORLD, YOU SLEAZY PILE OF TRASH!
ROMP!

AND WHAT HAVE YOU GOT IN HERE? ...PEOPLE ARE ALWAYS SAVING STUFF...

AH, LETTERS, PERSONAL LETTERS... LET'S SEE... LET'S SEE WHAT OTHER PEOPLE THINK OF YOU... "DEAR PEPITO: ...

"... THINGS ARE GOING PRETTY WELL HERE, EXCEPT FOR MONEY PROBLEMS. YOUR SISTER WAS PROMOTED TO THE SECOND GRADE"... LET'S SEE... LET'S SEE..."THEY SEIZED YOUR FRIEND LALO WHILE"...
I'm so smart!

MYOPIC.
... BANANA FANA FO FANA ME MY MO MANA... THIS ISN'T A LANGUAGE, JUST A LOT OF BARF.

AND THIS SHIT?... OH, I'VE GOT IT. IT'S YOUR SWEET PASSPORT.

NO, PEPE. THAT STUPID LITTLE BLUE BOOK IS YOUR SECURITY BLANKET, NOBODY'S GONNA TOUCH THAT.

MAYBE I KILLED HER ... AND I DON'T EVEN HAVE A DRIVER'S LICENCE AND NOW I'VE STOLEN HER CAR... I CAN'T BELIEVE IT...

IF I KILLED HER IT WAS SELF DEFENSE...

BUT SOMEONE WHO DOESN'T EXIST ISN'T LEGIT AND CAN'T EVEN DEFEND HIMSELF IN COURT.

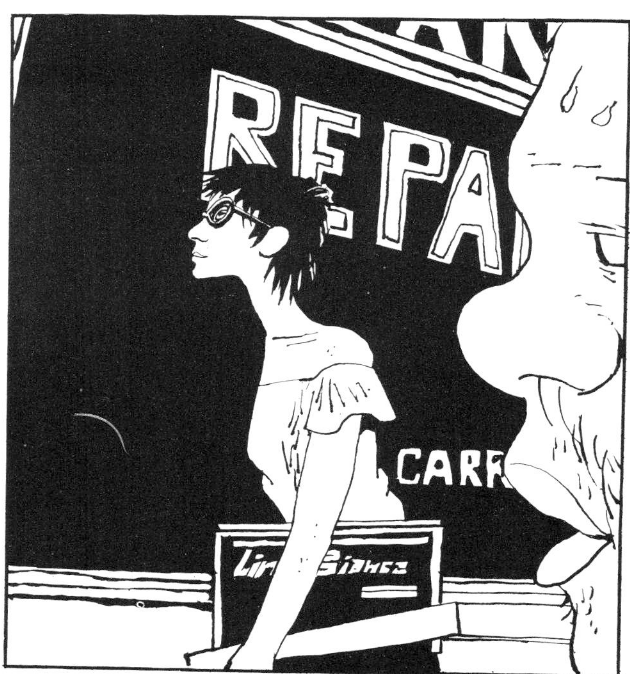
REPA
CARR

OLD ONE
CLUB

BUT IT'S SURE THAT PEPE EXISTS, HE FEELS THE NIGHT AIR FILLING HIS LUNGS AND KNOWS THAT HE'LL SEE THE DAWN OF ANOTHER DAY, THAT HE'LL SURVIVE, THAT HE'LL GET OVER THIS DAY HE REMEMBERS NOTHING ABOUT AND NEVER WILL REMEMBER ANYTHING ABOUT.

(I ARRIVE AT THE BAR OVER AN HOUR EARLY, IT'S THE ONLY PLACE I CAN GO...)

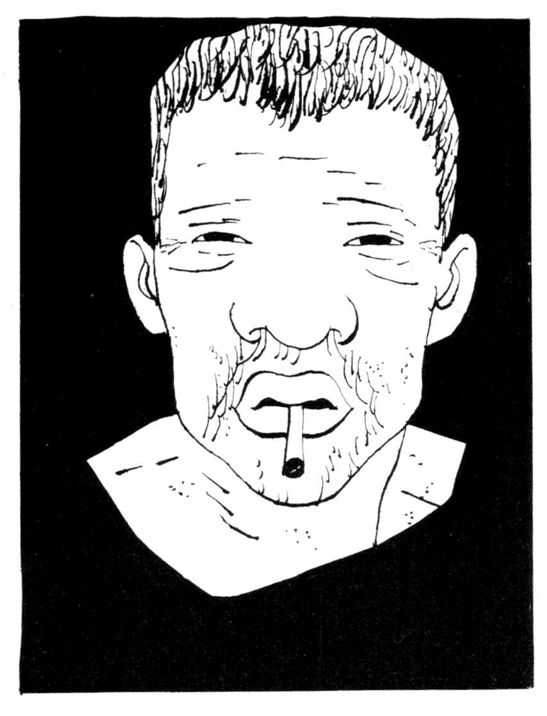

NOBODY'S GONNA CLEAN THE SHIT OUT OF YOUR PIGSTY TODAY, JOEY... LOOK AT HOW PLASTERED THAT BASTARD IS!

SCRAM!

WHADDAYA MEAN "SCRAM"? ... YOU PIG! YA KNOW WHO YOU'RE TALKIN' TO?... NOBODY THROWS ME OUT!... I COULD BUY TEN PIGSTYS LIKE THIS JUST WITH WHAT I'VE GOT IN MY POCKET. AND I'M NOT DRU...

HA, HA, HA, HA!! YOU COULD... WIPE YOUR ASS WITH THE MONEY YOU'VE GOT IN YOUR POCKET!... HA, HA!

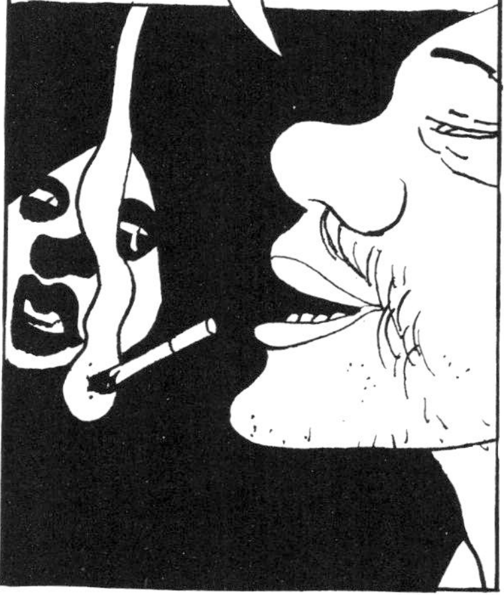

4 A.M.
WAKE UP, KID!

WHAT'S HA... PPENING ?. I ... BURP!... UH... I'VE GOT TO CLEAN UP... I'VE GOT TO CLEAN UP EVERYTHING!

NO PROBLEM. JONATHAN AND I HAVE ALREADY TAKEN CARE OF IT. DO YOU WANT ME TO GIVE YOU A LIFT HOME?
... NO, I DON'T ... I DON'T HAVE A HOME.

THEN WAIT HERE WITH JONATHAN.
HUH? WHO AM I SUPPOSED TO WAIT WITH?... AND WHY DON'T YOU TAKE ME HOME, BUT TO YOUR HOME?... OR ISN'T THE PEON GOOD ENOUGH TO...?

WATCH WHAT YOUR MOUTH, PAL!...

... YOU'RE DRUNK, BUT NOT THAT DRUNK...

... BE GRATEFUL FOR WHAT YOU'VE GOT! GOOD NIGHT...
... FOR WHAT I'VE GOT. SURE... NO ONE'S EVER GIVEN ME A DAMN THING.

WHAT A GUY, WHO'D EVER THINK THAT IT'S ... THAT IT'S ALL MY FAULT ... THAT GUY...
Marzia-ji Grill
DON'T WALK

... HE DRAGS ME INTO IT TOO. WHY NOT, WITH THAT SHITTY BAR I OWN...

... THAT GUY...!

... I SPEND THE WHOLE DAY SAYING YES TO EVERYBODY, AND IF I HAPPEN TO SAY NO JUST ONCE, ALL HELL BREAKS LOOSE ... LIKE WHEN THAT BIG WHORE ...

OKAY, SO HE'S AN ILLEGAL ALIEN ... SO WHAT ?
NY POL

HEY YOU ! ... WHERE'S YOUR I.D. ?

... THAT GUY...
AMERICAN. WHITE. NOT WANTED. EVERYTHING'S IN ORDER.

MEANWHILE, BACK IN THE BAR...
... AND SINCE WHEN?
THREE YEARS AGO...

I CAN'T BELIEVE IT, PAL... A WHITE ARCHITECT WHO'S AN ILLEGAL ALIEN IS WORKING AS CLEAN-UP PERSON... OH, MAN!... IF I TELL, NO ONE WILL BELIEVE ME...
WELL, THAT'S THE WAY IT IS.

WELL, YOU'RE IN GOOD HANDS NOW...
WHAT DO YOU MEAN, "IN GOOD HANDS"? WHAT IS THIS?

WHAT I MEAN... IS THAT NOW THAT YOU'RE A BUDDY, I CAN LOOK OUT FOR YOU... DON'T FORGET I'M A U.S. SOLDIER.
...I DON'T UNDERSTAND... I DON'T KNOW WHAT YOU'RE GETTING AT.
RUBBER TAIL INFLATED (IT SEEMS) WITH CENTRAL PARK'S AIR.

HEY... IT'S NOTHING, MAN!... THINK ABOUT IT A MINUTE: I'M A LAW-ABIDING CITIZEN WHO'S GOT A CLEAN SLATE... DO YOU FOLLOW ME?
YES.

IF I PROTECT YOU... IF I DON'T TURN YOU IN, I'LL BE BREAKING THE LAW LIKE YOU AND A LOT OF NEGRO BUMS THAT HANG AROUND HERE...
... I GET IT...
M
CASH N' CARRY
5
+
10
15

THAT'S THE WAY IT WAS!... HE WOULD'VE HAD TO HAVE UNDER-STOOD THAT COMPLETELY BUT HE COULDN'T...

... NO, DON'T DO IT... DON'T...
OH, YEAH?... HOW'D YOU SUDDENLY GET SO HUMANE?
People's Temple

... IT'S JUST THAT... I'M ALONE... WITH NO ONE TO...
People's Temple

NO ONE WHAT? NO ONE TO EXPLOIT?... NO ONE TO OPPRESS? NO ONE TO DESTROY?... YEAH... YOU'VE ALWAYS BEEN ALONE, YOU JACKASS! ... YOU AND YOUR AMERICAN WARS. I'LL USE YOUR SHITTY WARS AND YOUR MEDALS TO WIPE MY ASS WITH, ASSHOLE!...

BUT I GUESS THEY'VE BEEN OF SOME USE. THEY'VE HELPED ME UNDERSTAND THAT I'M ALREADY A PRISONER, IT'S JUST A MATTER OF APPEARANCES!... YOU CAN BRING ME ORANGES AND CIGARETTES, YOU JERK!
DON'T GO... I WON'T TURN YOU IN... IT WAS ALL A JOKE!

YOU'LL NEVER UNDER-STAND ANYTHING...

... YOU SPEAK WELL... BECAUSE YOU'RE A GUY WHO'S GOT SOME EDUCATION... IF YOU KEEP PUTTING ME DOWN... I'LL TURN YOU IN!

THE FRESH AIR OF A NEW DAY. PEPE GOES TO THE NEAREST PRECINCT. HE'LL TURN HIMSELF IN.

(TO BE FREE, FREE, FREE OF MY OWN NIGHTMARES. FREE OF THIS FUCKING OLD GOAT WHO NEVER STOPS WORKING AGAINST ME.)

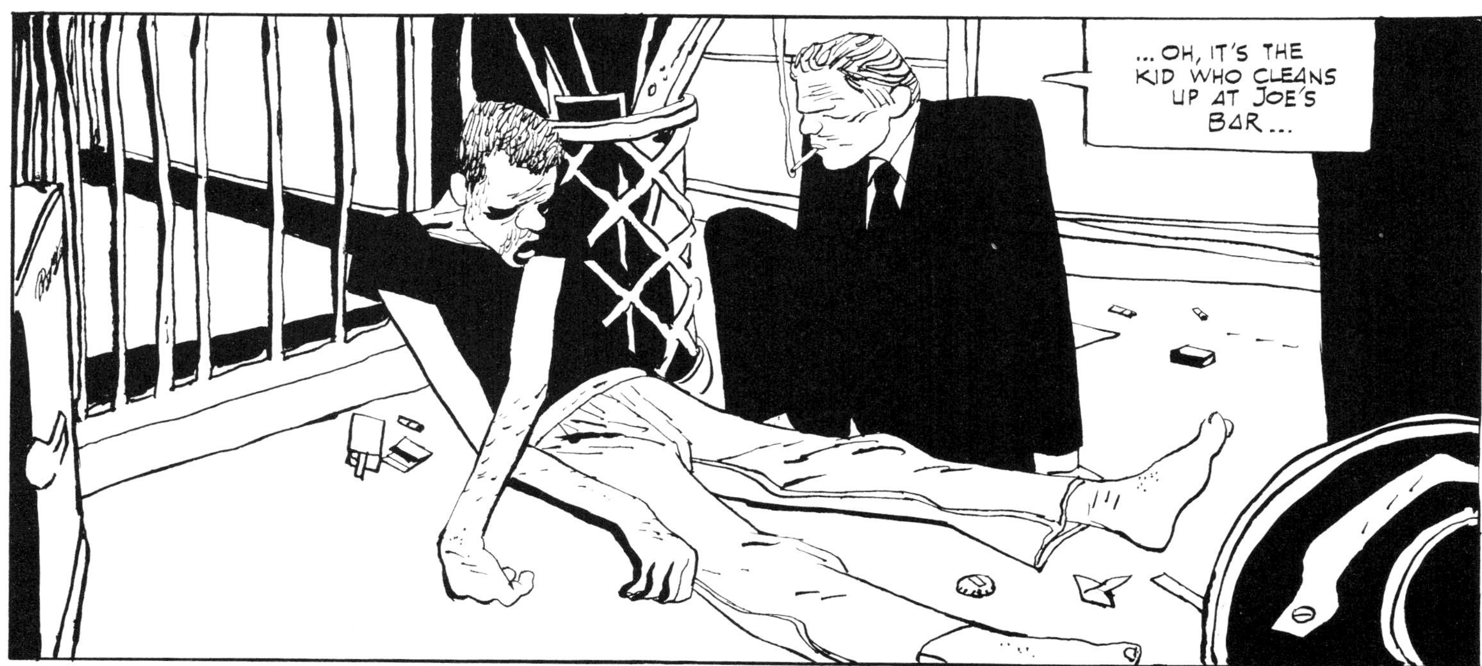

RUSTY STORIES

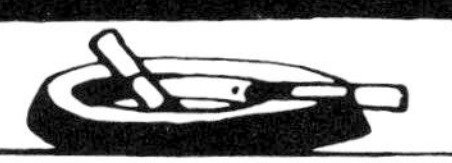

HEY... LOOK AT THAT CHEAP GUY!

... AND HE'S GOT A PARROT ON HIS SHOULDER. WHAT A STINK! THE WAY THESE PARROTS HAVE BEEN SMELLING LATELY.
HE MUST BE A PIRATE AND FOUND OUT THAT ALL PIRATES CARRY A PARROT ON THEIR SHOULDER. A REPULSIVE LITTLE BIRD FOR A REPULSIVE LITTLE CREEP.

SONS OF BITCHES... NOW YOU'LL FIND OUT WHO MOSES MAN IS!
A MAN WHO LIVES BY THE SWORD...

LET'S SEE WHO'S THE TOUGHEST.
Mountain man

LEAVE HIM ALONE! DON'T YOU SEE THAT HE'S THE GREAT MOSES MAN IN PERSON?

MR. MAN, I'M TIGRAN PACHA, WRESTLING CHAMP. I BEG YOU TO FORGIVE MY BOYS... THEY DIDN'T RECOGNIZE YOU...

2

YOU WERE A REAL CHAMP, THAT'S FOR SURE! EVERYBODY HAD TO KNEEL DOWN WHEN YOU PASSED BY...

MR. MAN, NO OFFENSE, BUT... HOW'D YOU END UP LIKE THIS? I MEAN YOU'RE A WORLD BOXING CHAMP...

ME... HEY... LOOK, I DON'T KNOW... EXCUSE ME, BUT I'VE GOTTA GO NOW.
GO NOW, GO NOW...

WAIT A MINUTE, SOMETHING JUST HIT ME. I'M GONNA MAKE YOU A DEAL...
ME?... ME?... ME?
...ME?

LISTEN GOOD. YOU'RE STILL FAMOUS, YOUR NAME'S GOT LOTTA CLOUT... WE COULD ORGANIZE A MATCH, YOU AND ME ... A MOCK FIGHT, OF COURSE...
BUT I DON'T KNOW IF...

LISTEN, I'LL GIVE YOU $ 3000 PLUS A PERCENTAGE OF THE TAKE...

$ 3,000 ?
$ 3,000, MINIMUM...
DOLLARS... DOLLARS?

3

For Moses Man $ 3,000 is a real fortune. And it makes him think back to earlier times when that much money was in the pot. Or even farther back, when $ 3,000 was an impossible dream. Now Moses needs some advice and no one's better for that than Uncle Will, his old, myopic coach. They meet at Joe's bar because Moses doesn't want to go to the gym.

4

THE STORY OF MOSES. TO TELL IT IS TO REPEAT IT, PLAYING THE SAME OLD SONG.
SPARRING-PARTNERS BADLY NEEDED APPLY HERE

HAVE YOU EVER BOXED BEFORE, KID?
"LUI"
NO, SIR, BUT THEY SAY I PACK A REAL WALLOP.

STORIES WITH ONLY ONE LANGUAGE.

...THAT KEEP REPEATING...

... EACH ENDING IS THE BEGINNING...

I.

IT'S A STORY THAT UNCLE WILL KNOWS BETTER THAN THE HERO DOES. THE KID'S JUST A SIMPLE ACTOR, SAYING HIS LINES, OUT OF TOUCH WITH HIMSELF AND HIS OWN EXISTENCE.

6

A LOT OF PEOPLE ASKED HOW SOMEONE LIKE MOSES, WHO WAS SO CLUMSY...
WHAT?
WHAT?

...COULD HAVE DEVELOPED SUCH A REFINED TECHNIQUE...

SUCH A SURE STYLE... SO ELEGANT...

...IRONIC...
THE WINNER!
OSES MAN

YES, A LOT OF PEOPLE ASKED THEMSELVES THAT QUESTION.

7

A FEW MONTHS LATER ...

8

WHEN THE STORY REACHES ITS CLIMAX, THE SECOND CHARACTER ENTERS, THE ONE WHO WILL WALK OUT OF IT ALL UNSCATHED. THE BLONDE, OF COURSE.

MOSES MAN WON THE WORLD TITLE AND THE BLONDE KEPT HER PROMISE. THERE WILL SOON BE A REMATCH WITH THE EX-CHAMPION AND MOSES'S STORY WILL BEGIN TO FALL APART.

10

THERE'S NO DOUBT THAT THIS TURNS INTO A LONELY STORY, BECAUSE MOSES IS LIKE AN OVERTURNED CUP, A SINKING SHIP. THE SHADOW OF THE OLD MOSES HOVERS AROUND THE CURRENT MOSES.

THE REMATCH.

ROUND ONE! THE TWO BOXERS IN THE CENTER OF THE RING. THE MOCKING EXPRESSION OF MOSES MAN, THE JEWISH MATADOR, PROVOKES THE EX-CHAMP...

MOSES COUNTS TOO MUCH ON HIS MAGNETISM, WHILE THE EX-CHAMPION SEEMS TO WAIT. THERE'S NO TRADING PUNCHES...

WHAT A RIGHT HOOK! MOSES MAN'S LEGS SEEM WEAK...!

...ONE... TWO...

C'MON, ZIM!
...SEVEN, EIGHT...

...WINNER BY A KNOCK-OUT IN THE FIRST ROUND! HE'S GOT THE TITLE BACK.
WHAT'LL YOU DO WITH HIM?
SEEMS HE WAS A REAL PUSHOVER ... HE WON'T EVER WIN THE TITLE AGAIN. LET HIM MANAGE HIMSELF.

12

GENTLEMEN, WE'VE GOT TO ARRANGE A MEETING TO SIGN THE CONTRACT.

A MONTH LATER, THE MATCH IS ALL SET. THE BIG DAY ARRIVES. MOSES MAN WILL MEET TIGRAN PACHA IN THE BIG FIGHT...

13

THE FARCE IS ENDING.

MATCH BETWEEN TIGRAN PASCHA AND MOSES MAN.

IT'S A GALA EVENING AT TIGRAN PACHA'S SHOW. (HIS REAL NAME IS AHMED ABDUL IBN BATOUTA). PROMISING THE CROWD A SPECTACULAR FIGHT, THE THEATRICAL ACTOR-FIGHTER HAS MANAGED TO FILL THE 3,500 SEATS OF HIS "STADIUM".

14

"Then it was the Siamese Twins' turn. They're the "Duo Duet" and it was all pretty disgusting, but you can't say it wasn't original."

Goo-oo, ga-ga...
Ughh...
The Duets!

"The Siamese on the left won..."
HIT 200

In the next match, the outfit's boss took on the earlier winners.

15

Tigran
Tigran!
AND NOW!... THE MAIN EVENT OF THE CENTURY...!

THE GREAT TIGRAN PACHA BRINGS ALL OF HIS PRESTIGE INTO THE RING AGAINST ONE OF THE BIGGEST CHAMPIONS OF ALL TIME...

MOOOSEEES MAAAANNNN! THE JEWISH MATADOR!
Moses Maa-a-a-an
"MOSES AND PACHA SHOULD HAVE ENTERTAINED THE SPECTATORS, MATCHING FORCES WITHOUT HURTING EACH OTHER. INSTEAD..."

16

"There was a profound silence in the arena as the fight began..."
H.J.

"It hurt to see man take part in a charade like that..."

"And the famous world ex-champion should have understood that...

So far... every-thing's gone like a dream.

"It was a helluva punch. The kind of assault the Moslem fighter wasn't going to forgive."
One... two...

17

"MAYBE HE FELT ALLAH WAS WATCHING HIM..."
THIS... WASN'T... WHAT WE AGREED ON... BASTARD...

"AND ALTHOUGH HIS REACTION WAS RATHER EXAGGERATED, IT WAS VERY HUMAN..."

I DON'T GET IT... THAT NUT TRIED TO KILL ME!

THINGS WERE GOING GREAT AND THEN ALL OF A SUDDEN... HE WAS OFF HIS ROCKER.

18

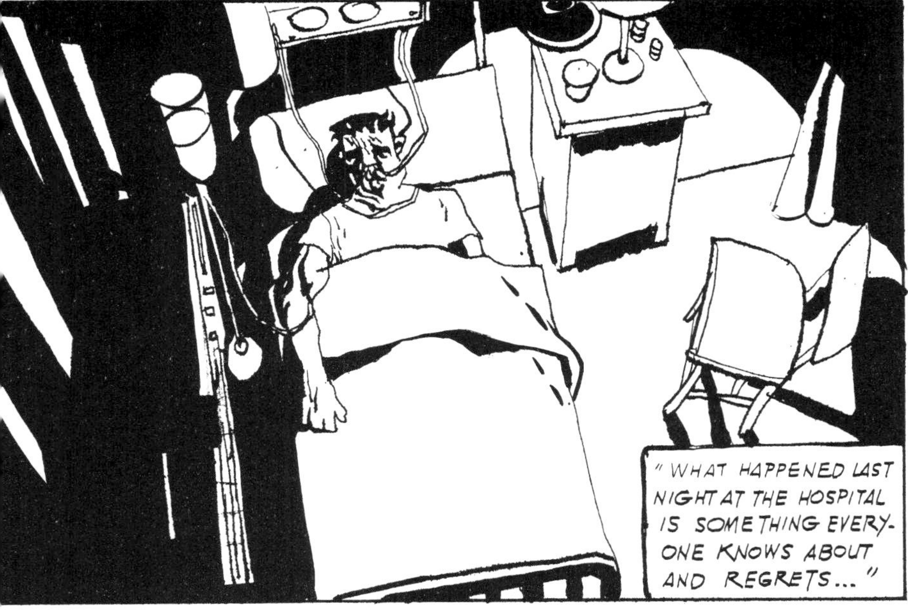

"MOSES MAN, THE JEWISH MATADOR, SUCCUMBED IN THE HOSPITAL. HE WAS THE VICTIM OF HIS OWN FISTS, THE FISTS THAT USED TO BE HIS MOST PRECIOUS GIFT. HE DIED BY PUNCHING HIMSELF IN THE LIVER TOO MANY TIMES..."

19

THIS STORY WITH ALL ITS TRITE INGREDIENTS IS A TRUE STORY. IT REPEATS ITSELF OVER AND OVER. THERE WILL ALWAYS BE PEOPLE WHO THINK THEY ARE INDESTRUCTIBLE, MADE OF METAL... BUT, LIKE METAL THEY OXIDIZE. LATER THEY RUST, ROT AND DISAPPEAR. EVEN THE HAZY MORAL SHOWN HERE AT THE END, CAN ALSO OXIDIZE, THEN VANISH.

ELLA

DARK ROOM
Joe's old Bar.
JOE'S
JOE'S
SOUVENIR from SITGES

ELLA CAPTURES THE TIMES SHE'S LIVING IN. SHE'S DECIDED TO BLOW UP ALL THOSE PHOTOS.

"COUPLE IN A BAR". THEY WERE BOTH ALONE, THE WOMAN HAD BEEN WATCHING HIM FOR A WHILE...

1

Cheryl Blues.
I'M AFRAID... MAYBE I'VE GOT A TUMOR...

TAKE ME TO A HOSPITAL!
TAXI CAB

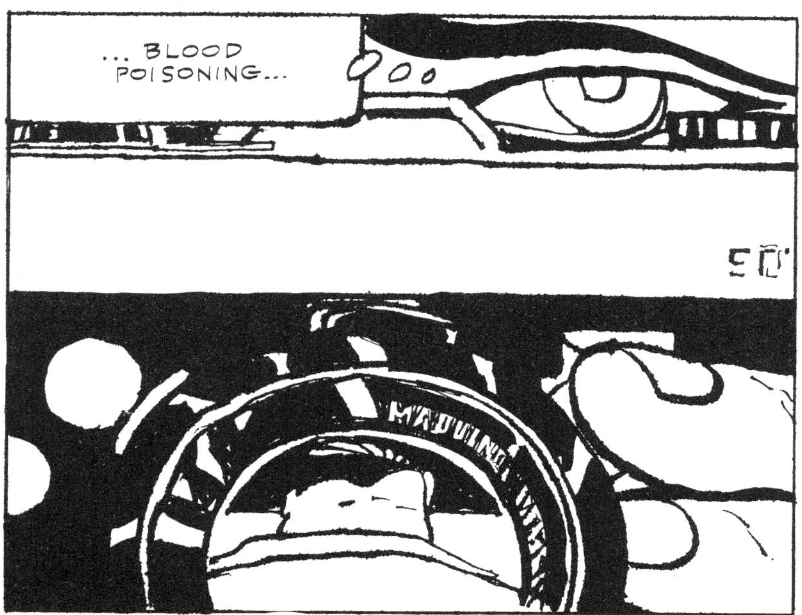
... BLOOD POISONING...

... A LIVER THAT DOESN'T WORK ANYMORE...

POOH!
... MAYBE THEY'LL BE ABLE TO DO SOMETHING...
TAXI CAB
Coblo Sitgito
BENVINGUTS

2

...WELL... WELL... TELL ME A LITTLE ABOUT WHAT'S WRONG...

Caminante, no hay ca- minos, se hace camino al andar...
I'M AFRAID I'VE GOT A TUMOR... I THINK MY BODY'S NOT FUNCTIONING...
andar hacien- do camino ca- minos sobre la mar.

FIRST OF ALL, TRY AND CALM DOWN... HAVE YOU HAD ANY TESTS... EXAMINATIONS?
YES, YES! A MONTH AGO... EVERYTHING WAS NEGATIVE...

3

OKAY, YOUNG LADY...
IT'S ALL OVER...

EXCUSE ME... BUT SOMETIMES I CAN'T CONTROL MY EMOTIONS... I DON'T KNOW HOW TO THANK YOU.

I DON'T THINK THERE'S ANYTHING WRONG WITH YOUR BODY... YOU'LL JUST HAVE TO GET A GRIP ON YOURSELF.

...YES, BUT I DON'T WANT TO CONTROL ALL OF MY IMPULSES... NOT ALL OF...

4

A YEAR AND A HALF OF PHOTOS OF PERSONAL STORIES. BUT THESE ARE PHOTOS SHE DOESN'T APPEAR IN EVEN ONCE, AS IF A QUICK LOOK IN THE MIRROR WAS ALL SHE NEEDED. THE MIRROR SHOWS HER IMAGE BUT ALSO HIDES IT.

THOSE EXPRESSIONS... SHE WAS LOOKING FOR A PARTICULAR FACE.

IT'S HIM!

GUESS WHO?
... IT'S... IT'S YOU...

DO YOU REMEMBER ME?... I'M...
I REMEMBER YOU VERY WELL. I'VE BEEN THINKING ABOUT YOU...
Como he pensado en tiiiiii iii...

...I'M GOING TO ADD SOME MAGIC INGREDIENTS AND BRING YOU TO LIFE, MY LITTLE PUPPET. I DON'T WANT TO KEEP GOING THROUGH LIFE ALONE.

MY EYES WERE ALWAYS FOCUSED ON HIM... PRETTY SOON I CAME TO HATE THE CAMERA...

HAVE YOU EVER MADE LOVE TO A WHITE WOMAN?
YES, AND YOU? ... I MEAN, WITH A BLACK MAN...

THERE'S A BOOK BY LEROY JONES CALLED "DUTCHMAN" THAT'S ABOUT A BLACK MAN AND A WHITE WOMAN RIDING THIS SUBWAY...

He rodao como bolita
de purrete arrabalero
estoy fulero y ca
chuzo por los
golpes que
vueltes...!
YES, AT THE END SHE KILLS HIM AND THEN SHE REPEATS THE WHOLE THING AGAIN WITH ANOTHER BLACK... WHAT MADE YOU THINK OF IT NOW?

MAYBE I'M A LITTLE BIT AFRAID THAT YOU'LL KILL ME. IT'S IN THE BACK OF MY MIND... IT'S BECAUSE I'M BLACK.
LOOK, IT'S THE DOCTOR. ISN'T HE LUCKY!

BOCHERINI CONCERTO FOR CELLO AND ORCHESTRA. THE SOLOIST IS PIERRE FOURNIER.

7

THIS DUDE MUST BE DOIN' PRETTY WELL ... MAMA ALWAYS SAID YOU GOTTA STUDY. LOOK AND SEE IF SHE WASN'T RIGHT!

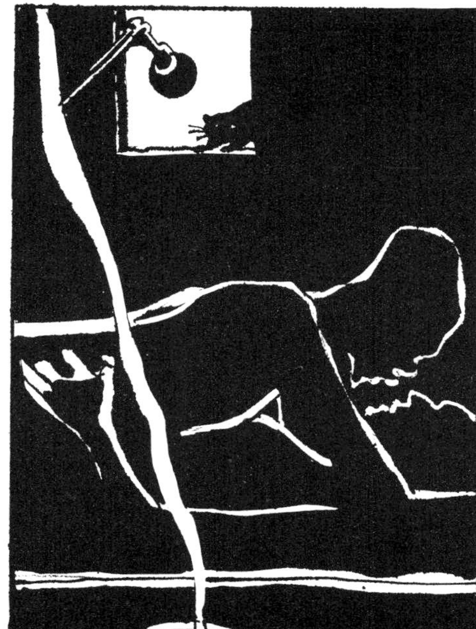

AHHH... MY LOVE, MY LOVE... MY LOVE... MY LOVE...

...IT'S KIND OF FUNNY THAT YOU WANT TO LEAVE NOW.
I WANT TO TAKE ADVANTAGE OF THE DAYLIGHT TO SHOOT SOME PICTURES...AND I WANT TO BE ALONE SO THAT I CAN THINK ABOUT YOU AND REMEMBER YOU.

YIPPIEEE!
...MORNIN'!
... SO HAPPY ...

8

I'D WORKED THE CRIME BEAT FOR A NEWSPAPER AND WAS USED TO SEEING DEAD BODIES, BUT WHEN I SAW THAT POOR BOY... I WANTED TO BREAK THE CAMERA, BUT NO... I WAS IN LOVE AND THAT WAS THE MOST IMPORTANT THING, I COULD CONVENIENTLY FORGET ABOUT EVERYTHING ELSE. WHEN YOU'RE IN LOVE YOUR CONSCIENCE DOESN'T BOTHER YOU.

WE SAW EACH OTHER ALL THE TIME...
... I THINK WE FORGET ABOUT ETHICS WHEN WE FALL IN LOVE ...
...DON'T EVER TELL THAT TO THE DIRECTOR OF THIS SLAUGHTERHOUSE.

... I'M HAPPY BEING WITH YOU, I SWEAR.
THAT'S WHAT EVERYONE SAYS ... BUT I BELIEVE YOU.

I WANTED TO HAVE A CHILD WITH YOU!
... I ... WANTED ONE... TOO.

UNTIL THAT DAY...

I HAD TO SEE HIM...
GOOD AFTERNOON, MA'M!
... AND HE WASN'T THERE. INSTEAD A MAN WHO LOOKED LIKE A MURDERER WAS STARING AT ME. IT SENT A CHILL UP MY SPINE AND I SENSED THAT SOMETHING WAS VERY WRONG.
MUÑOZ Y SAMPAYO

10

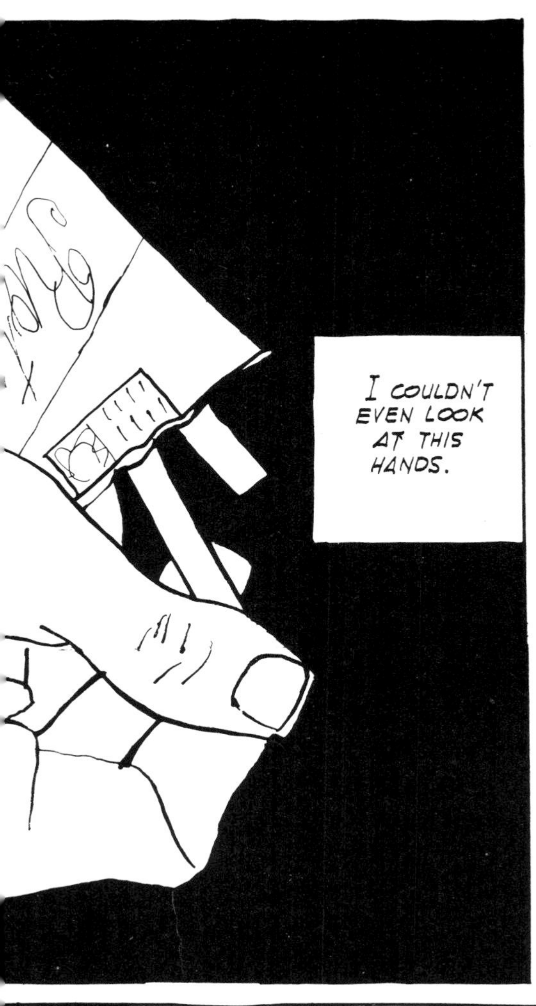
I COULDN'T EVEN LOOK AT THIS HANDS.

HE PUT THEM TO HIS MOUTH.

OH! I FORGOT MY WATCH.

IT'S FIVE THIRTY.

ABANDONED, COUNSELED, THREATENED AND FINALLY CAPTURED BY HER OWN WEAPONS, ELLA RETURNS AGAIN TO THE SECRETS OF THE DARK ROOM.

THEY'RE WALKING ALL OVER ME... THEY'RE ...

... MY BODY'S ROTTING ...
SHIT, SHIT!
Bocherini's

I'M SORRY, MISS. THE DOCTOR HAS NOT BEEN HERE THE LAST FEW WEEKS.
SHIT, SHIT!
LOVE ABOVE ALL

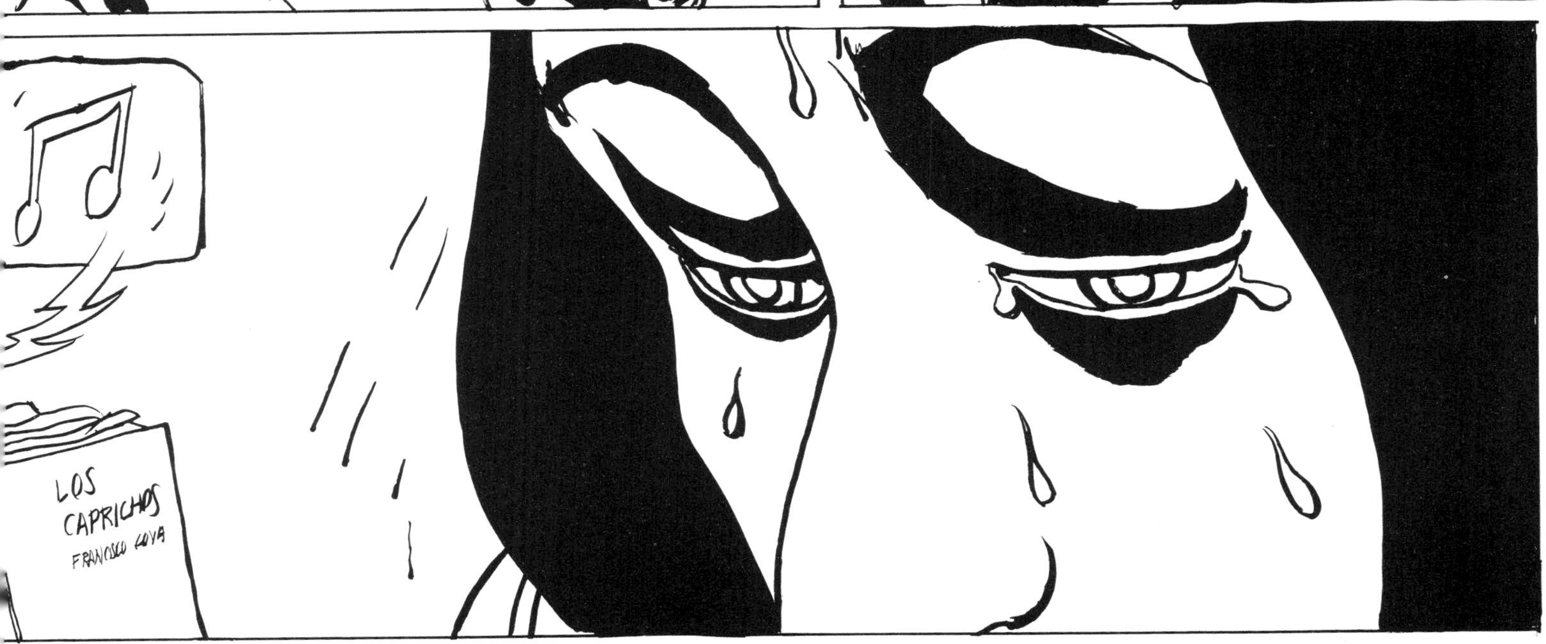
LOS CAPRICHOS
FRANCISCO GOYA

DEVELOPING PAPER,
LIGHT METER, DEVELOPER,
FIXER, BRIGHTENER.
I AM, ELLA SAYS, USING
OTHERS TO MAKE A
MIRROR OF MYSELF.

Ha!

HI... HI... I JUST CALLED YOU. I WAS WATCHING THOSE GUYS WHO...
HI... SOMETHING TOLD ME THAT YOU WERE HERE.

... I ... I TRIED TO FIND YOU.

I KNOW, I WAS OUTSIDE AND BESIDES... BESIDES THERE WERE CERTAIN THINGS I STILL COULDN'T TELL YOU.
LOOK AT THAT GUY. THEY'VE SURE DONE SOMETHING TO HIM. ... WHAT DO YOU MEAN "CERTAIN THINGS"?

YOU SEEM A LITTLE UPSET... SORRY, IT'S UNDERSTANDABLE... I...

LET'S GO SOMEPLACE ELSE... LET'S GO TO MY HOUSE. I WANT TO SHOW YOU A FEW PHOTOS THAT...

I'VE GOT TO TALK TO YOU, ELLA. I'VE GOT TO!
Odyseo... que expresión !!!

PRAY
YOU PICK THE MOMENT AND YOU THINK THAT IT'S ALSO GOT TO BE MY MOMENT. BUT NO. IT ISN'T MY MOMENT!... I WANTED TO SEE YOU, BUT NOT TO TALK, AT LEAST FOR NOW.

I THOUGHT THAT SOMETHING BAD MIGHT HAVE HAPPENED TO YOU... I'M LIKE A MOTHER... AN UNHAPPY BLACK MOTHER...
SOMETHING HAS HAPPENED TO ME.
Rape your head!

SOMETHING HAS HAPPENED TO ME TOO... TIME HAS GONE BY. I'VE MISSED YOU A LOT... WHY DON'T YOU WANT TO BE WITH ME ANYMORE?

THERE'S SOME-ONE ELSE, BUT THANKS FOR ASKING.

BLACK OR WHITE?... OH, EXCUSE ME!
THAT'S OKAY.

Que pena me da tu caso, lo tuyo es mental..

SILENCE.

SILENCE.

SILENCE.

ELLA SHUTS HERSELF IN, TURNS OFF THE LIGHTS, SUFFERS FROM INSOMNIA, DOES NOT EAT ANYTHING, ONLY GETS UP TO PISS. SHE NOTICES A RAY OF SUNLIGHT THROUGH THE WINDOW. SHE TAKES HER CAMERA AND LEAVES. A FEW DAYS HAVE GONE BY.

SHE GOES LOOKING FOR SOMETHING...
Arf...

SHE THINKS SHE'S FOUND IT...

UNTIL ...

... IT'S HIM !

SHE RETURNS HOME ...
" OLD BOXING STAR MOSES MAN COMMITS SUICIDE"... HE'S THE GUY I PHOTOGRAPHED AT THE BAR.

AND LATER SHE PUTS THE LAST PHOTO ON THE WALL.

OLD BOXING STAR KILLS HIMSELF

PASSENGER TICKET
AND

CLICK
CLICK!

FIFTH STORY

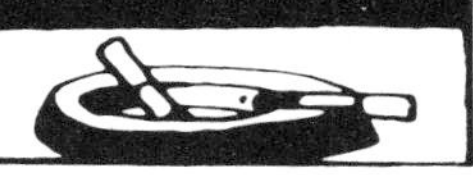

OKAY... LIKE YOU ALREADY KNOW, I'M ALWAYS THINKING ABOUT IT, BUT I COULDN'T TELL YOU THE WHOLE STORY. I JUST DON'T KNOW...
BUT I WANT TO KNOW WHAT YOU'VE DONE, CHICO.

WHAT I'VE DONE ?
... SENATOR KENNEDY THINKS THAT WE'RE LACKING LEADERSHIP IN THIS COUNTRY...
TURN THAT SHITTY RADIO DOWN.!! CAN'T YOU SEE HE'S TELLING ME SOMETHING..?!

TELLING YOU SOMETHING... I CAN'T STOP THINKING ABOUT IT, I CAN'T...
DAVID WEISS & SON

GOOD AFTERNOON, MR. WEISS...HI, MIKE!
HI... HELLO.

THANKS, MR. WEISS. SPEAK TO YOU LATER.

IT SEEMS THAT SHE'S SWEPT YOU OFF YOUR FEET, RIGHT?
EXPERTS DELCAPO

GO EAT AT JOE'S BAR, I'VE GOT TO GO TO THE BANK TODAY... AND DON'T EAT TOO MUCH!
YES, YES, OF COURSE.

WHAT A CHARACTER! HE FALLS IN LOVE AT SIXTEEN... THAT'S SOME BOY I'VE GOT!
ROSA... ROSA. I NEVER THOUGHT ABOUT HER BEFORE...
DRUG

... AND NOW WHAT DO I DO?

WHAT'LL IT BE...
SOMETHING REAL **KOSHER**... NO, A COUPLE OF EGGS, SALAD, HAMBURGER, CHIPS... COCA-COLA.

THE ONLY DAMN THING I COULD MENTION WAS THE GAME. WHAT ELSE WAS THERE?
TO INVITE HER TO?
YES, TO INVITE HER TO!
WHO, ME?
SURE... YOU, ME, WHOEVER!

THAT'S IT! YOU GOT IT! THATTAWAY!!
HUH?

HUH?

I'LL GET USED TO IT ALL TOMORROW.
BUT, MIKE, WHAT ARE YOU TALKING ABOUT, LITTLE ANGEL?

MAYBE... PARDON ME FOR NOT MINDING MY OWN BUSINESS, BUT IT SEEMS THAT... YOU ALREADY KNOW WHAT I'M GOING TO SAY...
THE TRUTH, MORE OR LESS.

YOU SHOULD REALLY MAKE UP YOUR MIND ABOUT THAT FELDMAN GIRL, SON. SHE LIKES YOU.
YOU THINK SO?
Rompe Saragüey
CLAPETTY-CLA

"TELL THE STORY, TELL THE STORY. I DON'T EVEN KNOW MYSELF HOW IT ALL HAPPENED. WELL, YES, I DO KNOW. I KNOW BUT I DON'T WANT TO REMEMBER. I DON'T WANT TO KNOW THE TRUTH RIGHT NOW."

I... OH, YOU SEE... MY FATHER WASN'T FEELING WELL. WILL YOU COME WITH ME? ... OVER TO MY HOUSE, I MEAN.

SED

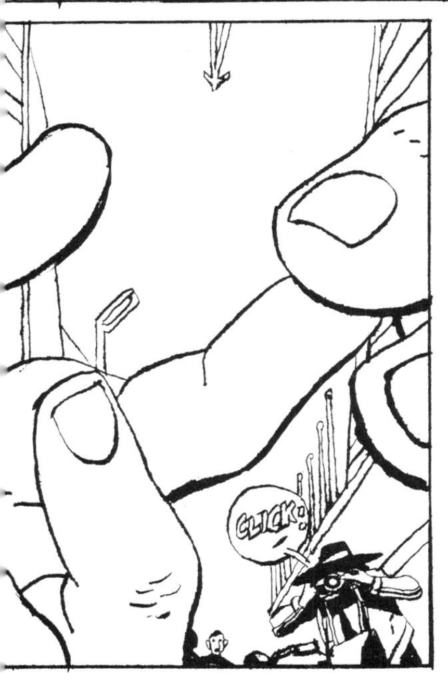

DAD?
MR. WEISS!!

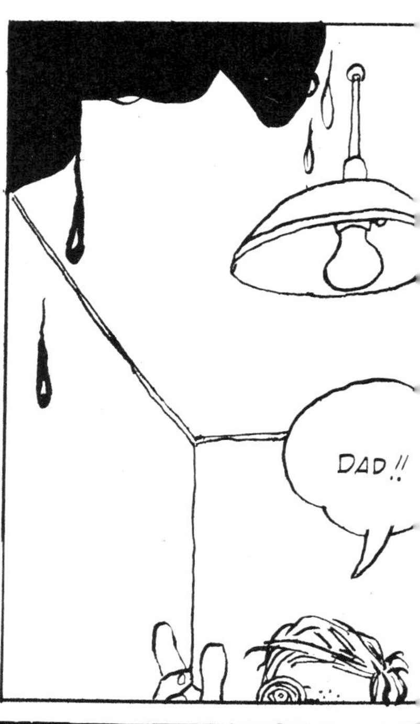
DAD!!

YES, DOCTOR BERNSTEIN. YES... YES... WE'LL TAKE CARE OF IT. YES, THANKS. SEE YOU LATER.

NO, NO, THERE'S NOTHING WRONG WITH ME. YOU SHOULDN'T HAVE CALLED THE DOCTOR. IT'S REALLY NOTHING... IT HAPPENS TO ME ONCE IN A WHILE.

HAVE YOU DECIDED YET?
HERE... PUT THIS THERMOMETER IN YOUR MOUTH.

NO, HE STILL HAS NOT MADE UP HIS MIND.

MISTER WEISS LIVES HERE... RIGHT?
NO SIR, HE'S NEXT DOOR...PARDON ME... IT'S THE PRAYER HOUR. WE HAVE TO PRAY.

MR. WEISS?
YES, YES, COME IN PLEASE.

HMMM... ?
DAD?

HMM... HMM!!

WE'LL HAVE TO RUN SOME TESTS AND TAKE X-RAYS... GO TELL YOUR MOTHER...
NO. I'LL TAKE CARE OF IT.

TWO DAYS LATER ...
THANKS FOR COMING WITH ME, ROSA. MIKE HAD TO TAKE CARE OF THE BUSINESS, YOU KNOW WHAT I MEAN?
JUST LIKE MY FATHER. HE COULD BE DEAD AND HE'D STILL GO TO WORK.

MEANWHILE ...
HI, KID! SHOW ME THE RUBBERS YOU'VE GOT HERE.
Mike's
RUBBERS?

AHA... AHAA... MAYBE THIS ONE WITH THE LITTLE HAND STICKING OUT OF THE END. DON'T YOU THINK THAT WOULD BE NICE, LEILA?

KEEP THE CHANGE, KID.
THANK YOU, SIR.
NO EYES

MAYBE I'LL HAVE TO USE ONE OF THESE WITH ROSA... BUT, WHICH ONE... THIS ONE... "ORIENTAL TORTURE"? OR THIS ONE...?
GIVE ME SOMETHING TO UNCLOG THE TOILET. THE SHIT'S UP TO THE ROOF.

THE NEXT DAY...
YOU CAN HAVE THE WHOLE DAY OFF, MIKE. HAVE A GOOD TIME, KIDS.

WHERE ARE WE GOING ?
TO YOUR HOUSE !

KILL
HANG THE SHAH
TO MY HOUSE ?... WHAT FOR ?
WHAT FOR ?
Rat, rat!
RAT-RAT!

OIL RISES 30%!

YOU KNOW SOMETHING ?... IT'S THE FIRST TIME THAT I'VE EVER...
ME TOO.

YOU ?...
I THOUGHT
THAT...
NO...

ONLY
KISSING AND
THINGS LIKE
THAT...

... THINGS
LIKE ...

I LOVE YOU.
I LOVE YOU.

THE NEXT DAY ...
MIKE... YOUR
FATHER HAS
LUNG CANCER.
WE HAVE TO
OPERATE ON HIM
IMMEDIATELY. I'M
SORRY, SON.
GUE

I... DIDN'T KNOW WHAT TO DO. THAT WAS WHEN I GOT REALLY HUNGRY, IT'S A HUNGER THAT'S STILL WITH ME. YOU KNOW WHAT I MEAN? I SWEAR THAT I COULDN'T DO ANYTHING EXCEPT EAT.

GIVE THE SHA!
... AND HE SAYS THEY'VE GOT TO OPERATE ON HIM IMMEDIATELY.
... AND IF WE DID THAT NO ONE IN THE WORLD WOULD RESPECT US... AND THIS WORLD IS OURS!

BREAK IT TO HIM GENTLY.
THE DOCTOR SAYS THAT YOU'VE GOT TO GO INTO THE HOSPITAL, ETCETERA.

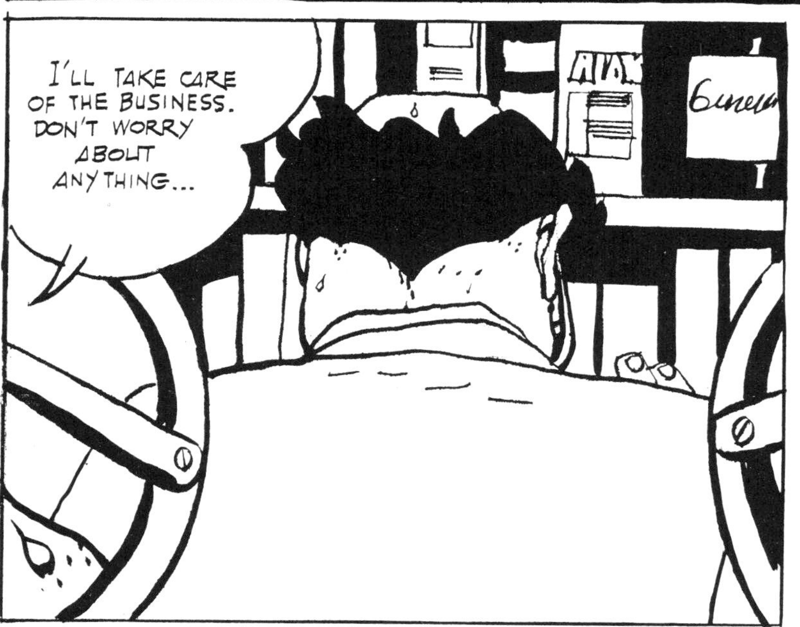
I'LL TAKE CARE OF THE BUSINESS. DON'T WORRY ABOUT ANYTHING...

ETCETERA. WHAT DO YOU MEAN BY "ETCETERA"?
OH, MR. WEISS... MIKE WANTED TO TELL YOU THAT...
STORE

YOU TWO GO FOR... FOR... A... WALK... I WANT TO BE ALONE!

OH, OH, OH... HHHHGGGG.

E DAYS WENT BY, I DON'T EVEN
EMEMBER HOW.
THE OPERATION DIDN'T GO BADLY. WE HAD TO REMOVE ONE LUNG, BUT...

I'M SORRY, SON. THE CANCER HAS SPREAD. YOUR FATHER ONLY HAS A FEW WEEKS LEFT.
BUT, WHAT?
I WANT TO DIE.
?
I DON'T WANT TO DIE.

I DON'T KNOW WHAT TO TELL YOU MIKE, I...
MY DAD... DAD...
...HOW COULD IT BE TRUE?
DAD!

MIKE... MY SON... MY BOY...
CALM DOWN, MR. WEISS. YOUR SON WILL BE ABLE TO VISIT YOU TOMORROW.

WHAT CAN I DO? ... WHAT CAN I DO?... WHAT CAN I DO?

MY FATHER GOT WORSE. I TOOK CARE OF THE BUSINESS.
YOU'RE REALLY GETTING FAT, MIKE... WHY DO YOU EAT SO MUCH?
ME, EAT? I HARDLY EAT ANYTHING AT ALL.

OH, MIKE... DON'T GET SO FAT, BUDDY... OR WE CAN'T GO ON DOING... DOING THESE KINDS OF THINGS...
I... I... I SWEAR, ROSA...

DON'T SWEAR... DON'T SWEAR... OH... OH...
ROSA!
GO HOME IRANF...KERS!
Patriots League
HOME OF AN IRANIAN FAMILY.

LISTEN TO THIS: "TODAY THEY STILL THINK THAT CANCER IS A SICKNESS CAUSED BY NOT BEING PAS- SIONATE ENOUGH AND THAT IT FINDS ITS VICTIMS AMONG..."
PUT THAT AWAY, MIKE. COME OVER HERE.

LIGHT!?
"... PEOPLE WHO ARE SEXUALLY OPRESSED, LACKING IN SPONTANEITY, UNABLE TO EXPRESS ANGER..."
I'M GOING.

WE NO HURT ANYONE.
"... WITH THESE PEOPLE THE CANCER ACTS LIKE AN UNPITYING SECRET INVASION..."

"...DIAGNOSIS...IT MEANS A TRUTH THAT WOULD BE DEVASTING FOR MOST, UNLESS THEY ARE EXCEPTIONALLY MATURE AND INTELLIGENT."
MIKE! EXCUSE ME...

YOUR FATHER IS DYING, BUT I THINK HE DOESN'T KNOW IT... DON'T LET ON THAT YOU KNOW, OKAY?
"IT WOULD BE DEVASTAT-ING."

HOW'S THE BUSINESS GOING, SON? ... WHY ARE YOU GETTING SO FAT?

I DON'T WANT TO DIE THIS WAY, YOU UNDERSTAND?
YOU'ARE NOT GOING TO DIE, DAD.

DO YOU UNDERSTAND, SON?

A FEW DAYS LATER...
HE GETS THINNER EVERY DAY... HE'S DYING...
ARE... ARE YOU SURE?

THE DOCTOR TOLD ME... AND DAD KNOWS IT TOO!

ROSA... YOU'D DO IT?... YOU'D KILL YOUR FATHER TO...?
OH... MIKE MIKE.

... I'D LIKE TO KNOW IF YOU'D DO IT.
OH, MIKE... YOU COULD HAVE HURT YOURSELF SO BAD... IF I'D DO WHAT?

NO... NO, NOTHING.
THEY SAY THAT OLD WEISS IS DYING IN THE HOSPITAL... OF "THAT".
THE BIG "C"?

It seemed like I wasn't even old Weiss's son anymore. I closed the business, you get what I mean? And then I just started wandering around. I didn't want to meet up with her again. I don't know how many days it was. I thought and I thought...

THE NEXT DAY I WENT TO SEE HIM...
WE'RE DOING EVERYTHING POSSIBLE SO THAT THE DOESN'T SUFFER... TRANQUILIZERS...HE'S GOT VERY LITTLE TIME LEFT.

HI, DAD.

HE WAS ASKING ME TO DO IT.

COME ON, DAD. IT'LL ALL BE OVER NOW.

. YOU FATHER LLER... YOU SON F A BITCH !!
YOU HORRIBLE MURDERER !!!

SNIFF..

THAT'S HOW IT WAS... I KILLED HIM BECAUSE... HEY, WHERE ARE YOU?
IN BED. SO SHUT UP NOW, PIG!!

MIKE.

MURDERER!
HEY... WHAT'S GOING ON?
MIKE.

DOG! MURDERER!
Grr.
... DEAR ROSA: I WAS SAVED BY A MIRACLE. I'M GETTING A LOT THINNER AND THE DOCTORS SAY THAT I'LL RECOVER. UNFORTUNATELY, I'LL BE BLIND. THE LAWYER SAYS THAT...

END